Virginia

SOL COACH

Strategic Reading

by
Stuart Margulies, Ph.D.
&
Maria Goudiss

Triumph Learning

019

Virginia SOL Coach Strategic Reading
ISBN# 0-87694-921-9
019

Triumph Learning®, 136 Madison Avenue, 7th floor, New York, NY 10016
© 2000 Triumph Learning, LLC.

10 9 8 7 6 5 4

Table of Contents

To the Student ....

You will soon take the **Virginia SOL Reading Test.** This test has many different types of questions. Sometimes the answers are not in the story. You will have to use your head to figure them out.

This book will help you to read better. It will help you to answer all of the many questions on the test.

Part I
Reading and Literature

NOTICE: Photocopying any part of this book is forbidden by law.

5

Unit 1 Basic Strategy

MAIN IDEA

The **Main Idea** of a story tells what is **most important** in the story.

Look at these pictures of Sue. What is the **most important thing** you learn about Sue?

You must look at ALL the pictures to find out.

Example 1

1. **The most important idea in <u>all</u> the pictures is**

   A. Sue has a nice smile.
   B. Sue likes to box.
   C. Sue plays lots of sports.
   D. Sue can swim.

   Your Teacher Will Discuss Your Answer

Read this picture story about Hank.

Decide on the Main Idea.

Example 2

2. **What is the Main Idea of this story?**

    A. Hank got a pet parrot.
    B. Hank keeps his parrot outside its cage.
    C. Hank wore a sweat shirt.
    D. Hank fed a seed to his parrot.

 Your Teacher Will Discuss Your Answer

STRATEGIES
TO FIND THE MAIN IDEA

1   Look at the whole story.

2   Decide what is most important.

3   Make the best choice.

Best Main Idea

Read these selections. Sometimes both of the choices are good. You must pick the best main idea.

Selection 1

People have always played marbles. It's a very old game. More than 200 years ago, when our country was young, marbles was very popular. George Washington was good at it. But marbles was also played 2,000 years ago by soldiers in the Roman Army. And we think it was played 10,000 years ago. Clay marbles were found in very old caves.

1.   **Which is the best main idea?**

   A.   Marbles is a great game.
   B.   Marbles is a very old game.

Selection 2

At first, Eric couldn't hit the ball. He would strike out every time. But he practiced a lot. His father used to pitch balls to him before school. Now Eric never strikes out. He hits balls to all parts of the field. He even hit two home runs in one day.

2.   **Which is the best main idea?**

   A.   Eric practiced and became a good batter.
   B.   Eric never strikes out anymore.

Selection 3

One hundred and fifty years ago, many families went to the Far West. They went so they could own their own farms.

They traveled almost 2,000 miles with their horses and wagons. Sometimes they got lost and starved to death, or they drowned in the big rivers. Some were killed in fights with the Native Americans who lived there. Some died from disease. It was a very hard trip.

3. Which is the best main idea?

   A. Many families went to the Far West.
   B. The trip to the Far West was dangerous.
   C. People wanted their own farms.
   D. People traveled with horse and wagon.

Selection 4

Sue has lots of friends. They like to do different things. Her friend Amy likes to skate. Tanya and Ann ride their bikes everywhere. Joya plays chess and Marge loves to read.

4. This story is mostly about

   A. how Sue's friends like different things.
   B. why Sue likes her friends.
   C . why Tanya and Ann like to ride bikes.
   D. why Marge is Sue's best friend.

Selection 5

Jenika, Kyle and Sarah go to school in Raleigh, North Carolina, but they each travel to school in a different way.

A school bus picks Jenika up each day. Kyle and four other students go to school together. A different parent drives them every day. Kyle's mother drives all five students on Monday. Sarah gets a ride on her father's motorcycle. She has to hang on tight to get to school every day.

5. **This story is mostly about**

    A. how different students get to school.
    B. why Sarah has to hang on tightly to get to school.
    C. how parents work together to take kids to school.
    D. which ways of getting to school are most fun.

STORY SETTING

Where and When

The **setting** of a story answers two questions:

- WHERE did this story take place?

        and

- WHEN did this story take place?

Sometimes the author tells you WHERE the story happened.

Sometimes you have to figure it out by yourself.

Look at the picture below. See if you can figure out where this happened.

Example 1

. . . .

1. **The setting of this picture is**

    A. a pet shop.
    B. the man's home.
    C. the street.
    D. an animal hospital.

 Your Teacher Will Discuss Your Answer

When you read a story or look at a picture, you can often tell **WHEN** it happened.

Look at the picture and tell **WHEN** it happened.

The setting of a story tells you both when and where it happened. Find the setting of the picture below.

Example 2

2. **The setting is**

   A. a city street on a summer night.
   B. a town street on a winter night.
   C. a city street on a winter afternoon.
   D. a classroom on a winter morning.

 Your Teacher Will Discuss Your Answer

STRATEGIES
TO FIND THE SETTING

1 Look for clues to tell you where the story takes place.

2 Remember—the setting includes both <u>time</u> and <u>place</u>.

Selection 1

Shamara picked up the ball. She felt sure of herself. She sent the ball high in the air. Then she watched as it dropped down through the center of the hoop. She put in five in a row without missing. Everyone stopped what they were doing. The weight lifters put their weights down. The people doing exercises stopped. Even the runners stopped. Everyone stopped to watch Shamara.

1. **Where did this take place?**

   A. in the school gym
   B. in the back yard

Selection 2

Mrs. Cooper and Mr. Hawkins liked to have coffee together. They both taught science and they liked to review what they were going to teach before the school day began. They also liked to set up the science lab so it was ready for the students in the first period.

2. **What time did Mrs. Cooper and Mr. Hawkins meet?**

   A. 8 AM
   B. Noon

Selection 3

The TV set was on. The evening news was giving all the sports results. We waited to hear if our team had won.

3. **The setting of this story is**

   A. the living room.
   B. a school bus.
   C. a classroom.
   D. a movie theatre.

Selection 4

You couldn't see any people. The cars seemed like little dots. You could barely see them. Sometimes you could see lakes or high buildings but not much else. We were really high and moving at 800 miles per hour.

4. **What is the setting?**

    A. the top floor of a big building at night

    B. a plane in the evening

    C. a big movie theater at noon

    D. the school lunch room at noon

Selection 5

Look at the picture.

Decide on the setting.

5. **The setting is**

    A. early morning in summer

    B. on a small hill in June or July

    C. in a toy store in early spring

    D. outside in winter

Selection 6

. . . .

The moon shone brightly on the water. The canoe slipped through the lake. Clarise could see lights on the other shore very clearly. It would be about five minutes before she got there. All the campers would be excited when she arrived.

6.   Where is Clarise?

A.   in a city
B.   in the country
C.   at a zoo
D.   on a ocean liner

CHARACTERS

Describing Characters

Characters are the people in a story.

The author tells us a lot about the characters in a story. For example:

•   If they are short, or tall, or thin

•   If they like playing baseball or jumping rope

•   If they are happy, or brave, or lazy

•   How they talk and how they act

•   How they change during the story

What does the author emphasize most about the character in this picture story?

Example 1

1.   This character

    A.   eats a lot.
    B.   is lazy.
    C.   works hard.
    D.   is very smart.

 Your Teacher Will Discuss Your Answer

Comparing Characters

The **Virginia SOL Test** often asks you to compare two characters in a story.

Look at the next picture story and decide how to compare the boy and the woman.

Example 2

2.   **How does the boy differ from the woman?**

    A.   The boy is poor and the woman is rich

    B.   The boy is not smart and the woman is very intelligent

    C.   The boy is fast and careless and the woman is slow

    D.   The boy doesn't like animals and the woman loves animals

 Your Teacher Will Discuss Your Answer

STRATEGIES
TO ANSWER QUESTIONS ABOUT CHARACTER

1   The author usually doesn't tell you if characters are honest or wise or
evil. You have to figure it out from the story.

2   Look for clues that tell you what the character is like.

Selection 1

The next passage is from the autobiography of Althea Gibson. She was at one time the best woman tennis player in the world. She was the first great African American tennis star.

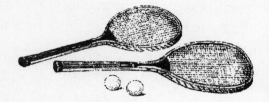

The only thing I really liked to do was play ball. Basketball was my favorite, but any kind of ball would do. I guess the main reason why I hated to go to school was because I couldn't see any point in wasting all that time when I could be shooting baskets in the playground.

I could fight, too. I was tough. I wasn't afraid of anybody.

—from *Always Wanted to Be Somebody*, by Althea Gibson, Harper Collins, 1958

1. **From this account, you can tell that Althea Gibson was**

    A. a hardworking student.
    B. a bully who picked on little kids.
    C. a tough kid who loved playing ball.
    D. a kind and friendly young girl.

Selection 2

The man speaking is describing Daniel Webster. Daniel Webster was a famous American. Read this description of him. What did people think of him?

You see, for awhile he was the biggest man in the country. He never got to be President, but he was the biggest man. There were thousands that trusted in him right next to God the Almighty.

—from *The Devil and Daniel Webster*, by Stephen Vincent Benet, Countryman Press, Weston, VT., 1937

2. **The author believes that Daniel Webster was**

   A. dishonest and evil.
   B. powerful and trusted.
   C. smart but a coward.
   D. shy but very funny.

Selection 3

King Midas was rich. But he wanted to be richer. He wanted to be the richest man in the world. He wanted everything he touched to turn to gold.

He got his wish. Everything he touched did turn into gold. Even garbage became gold when he touched it. But he couldn't eat. His food would turn to gold. When he kissed his daughter, she turned to gold, too. His wish had not given him what he wanted.

3a. **How would you describe King Midas?**

   A. generous
   B. very clean
   C. greedy
   D. hard working

3b. **How would you guess King Midas feels by the end of this story?**

    A. unhappy
    B. pleased
    C. excited
    D. bored

Selection 4

Mr. Bembarshi and his wife teach French, Spanish and German. Mr. Bembarshi used to be a professional wrestler and he looks big, tough and mean. But he teaches in a relaxed style. His students are always smiling. Mrs. Bembarshi is a small woman who looks very gentle. But she is very strict. Her students say she is the strictest teacher in the school.

4. **Compare Mr. and Mrs. Bembarshi**

    A. Mr. Bembarshi looks tougher and acts stricter than his wife.
    B. Mr. Bembarshi looks softer and is more relaxed than his wife.
    C. Mr. Bembarshi looks tougher and is more relaxed than his wife.
    D. Mr. and Mrs. Bembarshi are the two strictest teachers in the school.

VOCABULARY IN CONTEXT

Sometimes you don't know a word in a story.

You can often figure it out from clues in the story.

Suppose you read this:

> The man in Picture A is left-handed.
>
> The man in Picture B is right-handed.
>
> But the man in Picture C is <u>ambidextrous</u>.

Look at the pictures and figure out what *ambidextrous* means.

Example 1

 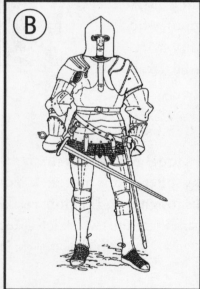 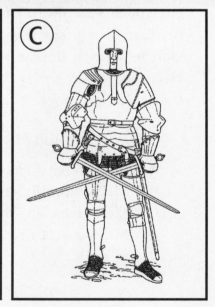

1. **A knight who is *ambidextrous***

    A. has very heavy armor.
    B. can fight well with both hands.
    C. is afraid of the enemy.
    D. won't go near water.

 Your teacher and class will discuss your answer.

Sometimes you can figure out what a word means from the words around it. Sometimes you can figure it out from the picture.

Example 2

. . . .

Alvin is good at *conjuring*.

 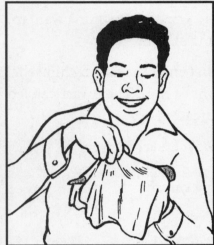 

2. **A person who is good at *conjuring***

   A. likes to eat carrots.
   B. is slow but strong.
   C. is usually quite old.
   D. does magic tricks well.

 Your teacher will discuss your answer.

Analyzing Phrases

Sometimes you may not know the meaning of a phrase.

See if you can figure out what it means to make a big splash.

Example 3

Mad Monster Max was a wrestler. He didn't want to be ignored. He wanted to be sure everyone was looking at him.

Mad Monster Max didn't enter the ring by himself. He came riding on a lion. And a dwarf walked in front of him. The dwarf carried a big red balloon which said: Mad Monster is the Greatest.

Max made a **big splash** wherever he went.

3. **A person who makes *big splash***

    A. is very quiet.

    B. can sing and dance and act.

    C. gets a lot of attention.

    D. doesn't care about money.

Example 4

Coach Larsen couldn't stop smiling. He could hardly believe his team had won. When the players went into the locker room, he was beaming with joy. He was **pleased as punch** with his team.

4. **Someone who is *pleased as punch***

    A worries a lot.

    B is happy.

    C is very tired.

    D likes to play sports.

STRATEGIES
FOR FIGURING OUT A NEW VOCABULARY WORD

1   See how the word is used in the sentence or picture.

2   See what meaning makes sense in the sentence or the picture.

3   Look at the answer choices. Pick the one closest to what you guessed.

Selection 1

Walker and Barley hadn't planned on doing anything much for the weekend. But then Teddy called and asked them if they were interested in going to a party at Cam's house. He said there would be a lot of food, and a bunch of different kinds of music, people, and even entertainment. "There will be an *assortment* of things there," he said. Walker and Barley decided it might be fun and went after all.

1.   **An *assortment* is**

    A.   a few things.

    B.   a funny joke.

    C.   a serious moment.

    D.   a lot of different things.

Selection 2

The museum explorers found bones of one of the largest dinosaurs. The bones were *gargantuan*. They wouldn't fit into the exhibit space. The museum directors decided they might have to build a separate, larger room where they could be displayed. All the kids from school went to see the bones.

2. **Something that is *gargantuan* is**

    A. broken.
    B. useful.
    C. old.
    D. huge.

Selection 3

Jillian and Harry went to the movies last Friday. The plot didn't make sense. Then the characters didn't act like real people at all. The movie was supposed to be about horses. But there wasn't a horse in the entire film. She didn't know what to make of the movie at all. The meaning of the movie was as *clear as mud*.

3. **Something that is as *clear as mud* is**

    A. uninteresting.
    B. funny and lighthearted.
    C. serious.
    D. hard to understand.

STORY PLOT

Summarizing a Story

The **plot** of a story tells what happened in the story.

A **plot summary**, or **summary** sums up the story's plot in a few sentences. Sometimes a story can be summarized through pictures.

- Look at the picture story.

- Then read A and B below.

Example 1

1. **Decide which plot summary goes with the picture story.**

   A. Mary got a bad cold. She didn't go to school. She stayed in bed for two days. Her aunt took care of her. Now she's feeling well.

   B. Mary likes to play soccer. She broke her leg. Now she has to stay in bed until her leg gets better. The doctor says she will be in bed for two weeks.

 Your Teacher Will Discuss Your Answer

Here is another example of plot:

Example 2

 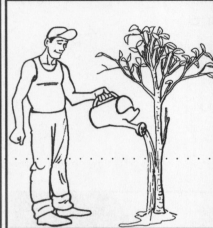 

2. **Which best gives the plot of this story?**

    A.   Victor likes beautiful flowers. He planted many flowers in his garden. He watered them. Now he has hundreds of beautiful flowers. They are red, green, blue, and yellow.

    B.   Victor bought a small apple tree. He planted it and watered it. Now he has a beautiful apple tree in his yard.

 Your Teacher Will Discuss Your Answer

Unit 2 Basic Strategy: Review

In this Unit, each picture story is followed by questions. Some questions review what you have already learned. Some of the questions are new.

Review Story 1

Looking

Catching a mouse

Catching a snake

1a. What is this story mainly about?

    A.   how owls learn to fly
    B.   what owls eat
    C.   where owls build their nests
    D.   how owls raise baby owls

1b. Where is this story set?

    A.   at night in the woods
    B.   at noon in the woods
    C.   at morning in a big house in the city
    D.   at night far below the ocean

1c. Which of the following plot summaries goes with the pictures of the owl?

A. Owls live on small animals. They are skilled hunters. They hunt at night. They eat small animals like snakes and mice.

B. Owls live in the woods. They live near water. They eat many kinds of foods. They live on berries and other fruit. They also eat frogs.

1d. The most important character in the story is

A. the moon.
B. the mouse.
C. the owl.
D. the snake.

Review Story 2

2a. Who made the sandwiches?

    A. father

    B. mother

    C. the oldest son

    D. the daughter

2b. The family took the train

    A. before they went shopping.

    B. before they ate.

    C. to go to the supermarket.

    D. before they made the sandwiches.

2c. Who is not a character in this selection?

    A. father

    B. mother

    C. a boy with a cap

    D. the family pet

2d. The best title for this story is

    A. The Family Visits Their Friends.

    B. Father and Mother Make Lunch.

    C. Sunday Is a Good Time For a Trip.

    D. A Family Goes On a Picnic.

2e. Read the following summaries and decide which one goes with the story.

    A. The Chung family is going on a picnic. Mom has shopped. She bought all of the food. Dad made the sandwiches. The whole family took a train to the place where they had a picnic.

    B. Mom and Dad like to play ball. They also like to watch ball games. Everyone in the Chung family is going to watch a ball game. They are taking a train to the ball park.

Review Story 3

3a. How does the cat feel in the first picture?

A. satisfied
B. hungry
C. stupid
D. cold

3b. How does the cat feel in the last picture?

A. hungry
B. stupid
C. cold
D. satisfied

3c. What would be a good title for this picture story?

A. The Cat Gets Supper
B. The Cat Sleeps A Lot
C. The Cat Eats Too Much
D. The Cat is Smarter Than Her Friends

3d. Read the following plot summaries and decide which goes with the story.

A. The cat was hungry. She scratched at the door to ask for something to eat. She got her supper and ate it. After that she was happy and rested.

B. The cat was in the house. She wanted to go out to play. But no one would open the door to let her out. After she ate she went outside to play with her brothers.

3e. Which of the following shows the correct order?

A. Cat gets food, scratches door, takes nap.
B. Cat takes nap, scratches door, gets food.
C. Cat gets food, takes nap, scratches door.
D. Cat scratches door, gets food, takes nap.

Review Story 4

4a. This story tells you

    A.   how the fish swims.

    B.   how the fish hides from other fish.

    C.   how the fish gets its food.

    D.   how the fish can fly.

4b. What happens in picture 2?

    A.   The fish is looking for food.

    B.   The fish is hiding.

    C.   The fish puts the fly on a tree.

    D.   The fish knocks the fly with the water.

4c. This story is set

    A.   in a lake.

    B.   in a swimming pool.

    C.   in a tub.

    D.   in a fish bowl.

4d. Which is the best summary of this story?

    A.   The fish likes to eat plants. The fish sees the fern or fine plants in the water. The fish eats all the plants then swims away.

    B.   The fish sees something good to eat. The fish shoots water at a fly and then swims over and eats the fly.

4e. This fish can shoot water with <u>precision and accuracy</u>. A ball player who shoots with <u>precision and accuracy</u>

    A.   is slow and lazy.

    B.   doesn't miss much.

    C.   uses only one hand.

    D.   makes a lot of errors.

Review Story 5

5a. This story is mostly about

A. why Jewell doesn't like her doll.

B. how Jewell's doll gets hurt and gets better.

C. why Jewell doesn't like to play outdoors.

D. how Jewell's mother fixed the doll.

5b. Which is NOT true?

A. Jewell likes her doll.

B. The doll's arm was torn.

C. Jewell threw her doll away.

D. The doll's arm was sewn up.

5c. How does Jewell feel after Picture 1?

A. angry
B. tired
C. sad
D. happy

5d. How does Jewell feel after Picture 4?

A. She is mad at her mother.
B. She is very unhappy.
C. She feels sleepy.
D. She wants to laugh.

5e. Compare how Jewell feels in picture 6 to how she feels in picture 4.

A. Jewell is happier in picture 6
B. Jewell is sadder in picture 6
C. Jewell is hungrier in picture 6
D. Jewell lost her doll in picture 6

5f. Which picture shows why Jewell cried?

A. picture 1
B. picture 2
C. picture 3
D. picture 5

5g. Read the following plot summaries and decide which goes best with the story.

A. Jewell was told to go to bed. But she didn't listen to her mother. She shouted and she cried. She tore her doll's arm. Jewell's mother put her to bed anyway.
B. Jewell loved her doll. She played with her doll. But she tore her doll's arm. Jewell cried very hard. Her mother fixed the doll and Jewell was very pleased.

Review Story 6

6a. How did Don feel when he saw his gifts?

    A. happy

    B. angry

    C. sad

    D. sleepy

6b. The best name for this story is

    A. Don's Friends.

    B. Don's Roller Blades.

    C. Don's Birthday Party.

    D. Don's Cake.

6c. Where does this story take place?

    A. in the backyard of Don's home

    B. in a room of a house

    C. on a farm 100 years ago

    D. in an amusement park

6d. Which of the following summaries goes with the picture?

A. Don, his brother, and his sisters are all at home. Don made his birthday cake. His sisters taught him how to bake. After he finishes eating, Don is going to the park with his friends.

B. Don was having a birthday party. His friends sang. Then Don blew out the candles. He opened his gifts. He was pleased when he saw his roller blades.

C. Don was 11 years old on Sunday. His parents and grandparents came to his birthday party. They gave him eleven birthday presents.

D. Don had a bad time on his birthday. He woke up feeling ill. He wanted to get a big coloring book. But he didn't get any gifts for his birthday.

Unit 3 Basic Strategy: Analyzing Stories

You will read three stories and answer the questions after them.

Selection 1

The owl is a hunter. It eats small animals like mice and snakes.

The owl has very good eyesight. It can see well even when there is very little light. It hunts at night when most of us are asleep.

The owl sits in a high place and looks for something to eat. It sees a small mouse running through the grass. The owl flies quickly and silently through the air. Soon the mouse is the owl's supper.

1a. When does the owl hunt?

    A. in the morning
    B. at noon
    C. at night
    D. on rainy days

1b. The story is mostly about

    A. how the owl learns to fly.
    B. how the owl gets its food.
    C. what the owl looks like.
    D. why the owl is so brave.

1c. The story does NOT tell us

    A. that the owl makes little noise when flying.
    B. that the owl can see very well.
    C. that the owl can dive into water.
    D. what the owl likes to eat.

Selection 2

Don was 11 yesterday. He had a big birthday party. His mother, his brothers, and his friends all came to the party.

First, they sang songs. Everybody sang "Happy Birthday" to Don. Then Don blew out the candles on his cake. Each person ate some of the birthday cake.

Don got a lot of birthday gifts. He got fast in-line skates from his grandmother and grandfather. He wanted to go rollerblading after the party, but it was getting dark.

2a. The selection mostly describes

    A. what Don got from his grandparents.

    B. what happened at Don's birthday party.

    C. who came to the party.

    D. the songs everyone sang.

2b. Which is probably true?

    A. Don had a good time at his party.

    B. Don's brothers ate too much cake.

    C. Don has two brothers and a baby sister.

    D. Don doesn't like to rollerblade.

2c. This story probably took place

    A. before breakfast.

    B. just after breakfast.

    C. late in the afternoon.

    D. late at night.

Selection 3

. . . .

We call our cat Gee-Gee. She got the name because she is a genius. She's more than a genius. She is a very smart genius. A Genius-Genius. That's why we call her Gee-Gee.

Gee-Gee gets her supper at 6 PM almost every night. Sometimes we forget to give her supper. Then Gee-Gee scratches on the door to remind us. Yesterday we forgot to put out her meal. At 6:15 PM she started to scratch the door. But we were all watching the World Series on TV, and no one heard her.

Gee-Gee was hungry, and she was angry that we forgot her meal. So she started to swing her behind hard against the door. Bang! Bang! Bang! Bang! We heard the door shake. It sounded like a big drum. Melody went out to feed her. A half-hour later, the game ended. We all went out and saw Gee-Gee was asleep. Her face looked very happy.

3a. A good title for this story is

    A. The World Series.
    B. Gee-Gee Gets Her Supper.
    C. Asleep with a Big Smile.
    D. We All Eat Supper.

3b. Which happened first?

    A. Gee-Gee ate her supper.
    B. Gee-Gee fell asleep.
    C. Gee-Gee scratched the door.
    D. Gee-Gee hit the door with her behind.

3c. Gee-Gee got her name because she is

    A. lazy.
    B. happy.
    C. old.
    D. smart.

3d. **This story takes place**

    A. at a World Series baseball game.

    B. in an apartment or house.

    C. in a hospital for sick cats.

    D. in a pet shop.

Part II
Previewing the Selection

NOTICE: Photocopying any part of this book is forbidden by law.

45

Unit 4 Analyzing Pictures and Titles

PREDICT STORY CONTENT

Sometimes you can tell a lot about a story before you read it.

Stories may have

- an introduction

- a picture

- a title

All of these things tell you something about what the story will cover. A good reader will be able to predict what the story will be about.

Look at Example 1.

- Read the introduction and the title.

- Look at the picture.

- Then decide what the story will be about.

Example 1

A Birthday Surprise

People get presents on their birthday. Sometimes the gift is just perfect.

1. **What do you think this story will be about?**

    A. John got a bat for his birthday. He always gets a bat.
    B. John's puppy ate his birthday present. John was unhappy.
    C. John got a dog for his birthday. He wanted a dog more than anything.
    D. John got 2 adorable kittens. They were beautiful.

Choice C is correct. This story probably tells that John got a dog for his birthday. It was a surprise. The introduction tells us the present was perfect. The title says it was a surprise. The picture shows a dog. So we can guess John got a surprise gift for his birthday; a dog.

If you look at the introduction, the title, and the picture, you can guess what the story will be about. You can't know for sure unless you have read the story. The introduction, the title, and the picture can help you to think about the story, and to make an inference.

Look at Example 2 and see if you can answer question 2a.

Example 2

We must take care of our teeth. Brush them every day. Go to the dentist for an examination.

Jed's Terrible Day

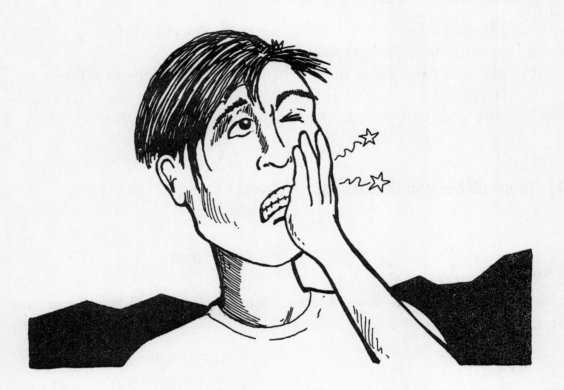

2a. Predict what the selection will cover.

A. The Christmas party in school.
B. Jed's toothache.
C. Why Jed likes Helen so much.
D. Jed's science test.

 Your Teacher Will Discuss Your Answers

What Questions Will the Story Answer?

Reread the introduction to this story. Look at the picture and the title. Then see if you can answer question 2b.

2b. Which sentences might be in this story?

A. Jed was a fast runner, but he had never been in a race before.
B. Jed hated tests. Spelling was his worst subject.
C. Jed's father was a dentist. He lived far away because he was in the Navy.
D. Jed's tooth hurt when he woke up. It hurt more later in the day.

 Your Teacher Will Discuss Your Answers

Look at Example 3.

Write what you think the selection will be about. Your teacher will talk about your answers.

Example 3

The Fiercest Hunter of All

T. rex was the most ferocious dinosaur of all time. Its teeth were large and sharp. Its claws were like knives.

3. **What might you learn about in this story?**

   A. how *T. rex* hunted and ate other animals
   B. how the dinosaurs cared for their babies
   C. why there are no living dinosaurs
   D. how *T. rex* could swim

 Your Teacher Will Discuss Your Answers

Example 4

Earthworms can be a big help in your garden.

The Farmer's Friend

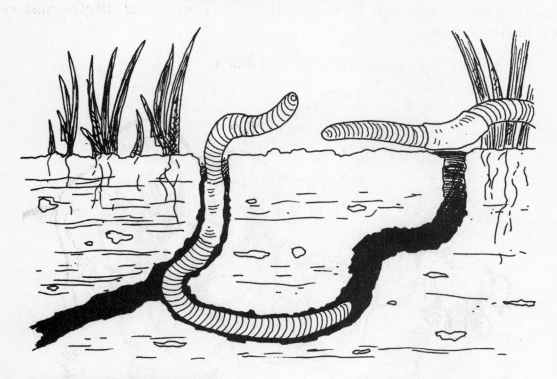

4. **Read Paragraphs A and B.**

Paragraph A

   Moles eat earthworms. They dig burrows underground. A burrowing mole raises a mound on the ground. People don't like these mounds on their lawn.

Paragraph B

   Earthworms crawl underground. They loosen the soil. This helps the plants to grow better. We can see earthworms after it rains, and they come out of their holes.

Which paragraph would go with this introduction, picture, and title?

   ( ) Paragraph A
   ( ) Paragraph B

 Your Teacher Will Discuss Your Answers

Read the next 5 selections. See if you can tell what the selections will be about.

Selection 1

Imagine a world without elephants. We would all have lost a great friend. All of us must try to save the remaining elephants.

The Last Elephant

1. **This selection probably tells**

    A. how elephants can pick things up with their long trunks.
    B. how people can find out how much elephants weigh.
    C. why the earth has too many elephants.
    D. how we can save the elephants from dying out.

Selection 2

Salvador and Anna said this was the most important day of their lives.

A New Life

2. **What question will this selection answer?**

   A. What are Salvador and Anna's favorite foods?

   B. Do Salvador and Anna own a cat or a dog?

   C. Do Salvador and Anna like each other?

   D. Do Salvador and Anna have many friends?

Selection 3

Kato was a diver. And there were dangerous sharks in the water.

Swimming with Sharks

3. **What sentence might you find in this selection?**

    A. Kato was a brave man who feared nothing in the sea.

    B. Kato was growing old, but he still swam every day.

    C. Many divers, like Kato, grew rich from their work.

    D. Kato was a slow swimmer because his arms were weak.

Selection 4

Slaves were free after the Civil War. Many went to the West to find work.

Black Cowboys

4. **Read Paragraphs A and B.**

Paragraph A

Abner Doland was born a slave in Arkansas. When the Civil War ended he was free. He and his family went to Montana. He learned to ride a horse and milk cows. He worked there for the rest of his life.

Paragraph B

Jack Curtis lived in Montana. His parents died when he was two. He had a hard life. He got in with a bad crowd when he was 19. Like most outlaws, he spent much of his life in jail.

Which paragraph would go with this introduction, picture, and title?

( ) Paragraph A
( ) Paragraph B

Selection 5

People in different countries grow different foods. Each country has its own favorite foods.

Supper All Over the World

Hamburger and French Fries

Noodles

Rice and Beans

5.   **What question will the story answer?**

   A.   How did people first learn to cook?
   B.   How can medicine help sick people?
   C.   What foods are eaten in different countries?
   D.   Why do people eat fish?

Selection 6

Keep cleaning solutions away from children.

Watch Out!

6. **Read paragraphs A and B. Which paragraph is most likely to be found in the selection?**

Paragraph A

Cleaning products are expensive. Sometimes children spill them on the floor. This wastes a lot of money.

Paragraph B

Some cleaning products look like they can be eaten. Children could drink something and get sick. Cleaning solutions can be very dangerous to children.

( ) Paragraph A
( ) Paragraph B

Selection 7

Dangerous Sports

7.   Read Paragraphs A and B.

Paragraph A

Hundreds of years ago the Maya Indians played a game like football. They used a solid rubber ball. The players tried to get the ball through a ring without using their hands.

Boxing and karate also have long histories. The ancient Greeks boxed. Karate goes back to Chinese methods of fighting that are over a thousand years old.

Paragraph B

It's easy to get hurt playing football. Knees, ankles, and shoulders are very easily damaged.

Injuries in karate are common. A hard blow must be blocked correctly. Boxing is another sport where people can get hurt. Blows to the head are especially dangerous.

Which paragraph would go with these pictures and title?

( ) Paragraph A
( ) Paragraph B

Part III
Inference and Higher Order Strategies

Unit 5 Basic Inference

Suppose Mary has a big smile on her face. We can infer she is happy. If Mary goes around smiling, we make the inference she is happy. An inference is a smart guess.

Suppose Mary has a spelling test at 10 a.m. Just before the test, Mary looks worried. After the test she looks excited. We can infer Mary did well on the test.

Suppose Mary looks like she is in pain. Suppose her fingers are all in bandages. We can infer that Mary's fingers are hurting. We can't be sure, but we can make a good guess. An inference is a good guess.

Part III of this book gives you practice in making inferences. Many of the questions on reading tests ask you to make inferences. When you finish Part III of this book, you will be able to answer most of the inference questions on reading tests.

Read the following short selections, and figure out the correct inferences.

Selections

1. **The girls are very hungry.**

   A. They didn't eat lunch.
   B. They didn't get much sleep.

2. ***Quad*** **means four.**
   Which is a quadrangle?

   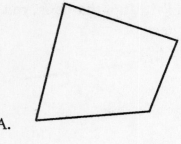

   A.

   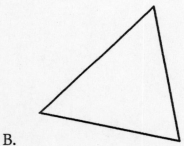

   B.

3. **Most fish cannot close their eyes.**

   A. Fish sleep with their eyes closed.
   B. Fish sleep with their eyes open.

4. **Cactus plants don't need much water to live.**

   A. A cactus plant can live in dry places.
   B. A cactus plant can live in dark places.

5.   We went to the movies. We laughed for two hours.

   A.   The movie was hard to understand.
   B.   The movie was funny.

6.   Someone bought two pictures painted by a painter named Van Gogh. They each cost 5 million dollars!

   A.   Van Gogh's pictures cost a lot of money.
   B.   Van Gogh's pictures are cheap.

7.   I like going to school. That's because I sit next to Lois.

   A.   I like Lois.
   B.   I hate Lois.

8.   That ice-cream looks delicious, and vanilla is my favorite flavor. But I can't eat another bite now.

   A.   I am not hungry anymore.
   B.   I want to eat supper.

9.   I went on a hike in the woods with my sister. We saw a small garter snake on the road. Sis said that they don't bother anyone. But I didn't want to go on a hike with a lot of snakes around. I went home.

   A.   I like snakes.
   B.   I am afraid of snakes.

10. First I put on my warmest underwear. Then I got dressed in a heavy shirt and pants and a thick sweater. Then I put on a big jacket and a hat and gloves.

   A.   It's important to be well dressed for the beach.
   B.   It was very cold outside.

11. Fred's sister told the teacher what Fred had done. Fred got in trouble. He was angry with his sister for telling the teacher.

   A.   Fred's sister told the teacher something bad about Fred.
   B.   Fred's sister told the teacher something good about Fred.

PRACTICE IN BASIC INFERENCE

The sentences in the boxes are true.

Figure out if the sentence below the box is also true.

- If the sentence below is true, circle YES.

- If the sentence is wrong, circle NO.

Selections

| It is always hot in Miami. |

The people in Miami get a lot of sun.

 YES NO

1. | Pears grow on trees. |

You dig for pears in the ground.

YES NO

2. | Gouda is a cheese. |

People eat Gouda.

YES NO

3. | The Atlantic is an ocean. |

You find tigers in the Atlantic.

YES NO

4.
> Astronomy is the study of stars.

An astronomer studies the stars.

YES   NO

5.
> Many doctors study one branch of medicine.
> A cardiologist is a heart doctor.
> A dermatologist is a skin doctor.

Jason had a rash on his skin. He should go to a cardiologist.

YES   NO

6.
> My grandfather was born in 1935.

His grandfather was born in 1960.

YES   NO

7.
> Mary-Ellen is my oldest sister.

Mary-Ellen is older than my sister Rosemarie.

YES   NO

8.
> Jed was a fast runner. But yesterday was the first time he ran in a race.
> He finished in 3rd place.

Jed won a race last week.

YES   NO

9.
> Babe Ruth was a great baseball star. He hit 60 home runs in one season. That was the record until Roger Maris broke it in 1961. Then in 1998, Mark McGwire broke the record of 62 set by Maris.

McGwire hit more than 62 home runs in 1998.

YES   NO

10.
> We are all planning a birthday party for Rosa. She will be 16 in four months and three days. We are going to rent a big boat for her party and invite all her friends.

This month, Rosa is still 15.

YES   NO

11.
> Jack has been my best friend since we were 6. Last year, his family moved into our building. He lives one floor above me. Now we can do our homework together and hang out.

Jack and I never see each other now.

YES   NO

12.
> Mrs. Rose liked to sing. She sang in a loud voice from early in the morning until late at night. Her neighbor was on old man named Mr. Harvey. He asked Mrs. Rose to stop singing. He said he couldn't sleep when Mrs. Rose sang.

Mr. Harvey liked to hear Mrs. Rose sing.

YES   NO

Unit 6 Further Work with Inference

USING PRIOR EXPERIENCE

Sometimes the answers to questions are right there in the story, and sometimes the answers aren't so obvious. You know a lot about people and a lot about life. Use all you know about the world to answer these questions.

Read Example 1 and figure out the answer to the question.

Example 1

1. **Lucy felt very happy. When she walked down the street, she was**

   A. crying.
   B. frowning.
   C. smiling.
   D. snoring.

The best choice is **C.** Lucy was probably smiling. The selection says that she was happy, so she might be smiling. None of the other choices fit.

You know a lot about how things work in the world. You may have to use some of what you already know to figure out the answers to the questions.

Find the answer to the next question. It's about sweaters.

Example 2

My mother gave me a sweater. It's a heavy sweater. It's made of very thick wool.

2. **The sweater**

   A. fits very well.
   B. is warm.
   C. is very long.
   D. has nice colors.

The correct choice is **B.** The sweater is warm. You can figure it out from what you know. The sweater is heavy. It is made of thick wool. That makes it warm.

Read Example 3. Figure out what Mark would do to get what his father needed.

Example 3

Mark's father wanted to shave. He didn't have any shaving cream. He asked Mark to go get some.

3.   What did Mark do?

   A.   He went to the movies.
   B.   He went to the drug store.
   C.   He went to the garage.
   D.   He went to the shoe store.

The selection doesn't tell you where Mark would go to buy shaving cream. But you can figure it out.

 Your Teacher Will Discuss Your Answers

Read the next selections.

The answers may not be in the selections.

But you can figure them out.

Read the following selections and figure out the answers to the questions.

Selection 1

We heard a lot of noise. We saw Maria crying. She was holding her knee and elbow.

1. **What probably happened?**

    A. Maria cooked cheese and eggs.
    B. Maria saw a movie about a monster.
    C. Maria fell down the stairs.
    D. Maria called her friend on the telephone.

Selection 2

The movie was just for adults over 18. Mark wanted to go to the movies. They didn't let Mark into the movies.

2. **Why not?**

    A. He was too tall.
    B. He was too young.
    C. He was too noisy.
    D. He was too happy.

Selection 3

It was very hot. Dad knew I didn't want to eat much.

3. **What did Dad make for my lunch?**

    A. He made a small sandwich.
    B. He made soup and chicken and pie.
    C. He made three cheeseburgers.
    D. He made spaghetti and meatballs, salad, and vegetables.

Selection 4

The kids were quiet. They were all staring at the screens and punching buttons. But the room was noisy. Lights were flashing on and off everywhere.

4. Where did this happen?

    A. in the school lunchroom
    B. in a video arcade
    C. in a large grocery store
    D. on a busy beach near a lake

Selection 5

During the first month of basketball, Shawna couldn't score very many points. The ball went too high or too far to the left. She only scored 2 points in 10 shots.

But she kept at it. By the second month, she was getting 7 out of 10 shots in the basket. All the work she put in really paid off.

5. Why does Shawna play better in the second month?

    A. Shawna grew 5 inches.
    B. Shawna practiced a lot.
    C. Shawna combed her hair and wore different clothes.
    D. Shawna studied 10 spelling words every day.

Selection 6

Mark went to the restaurant at 5:45 AM. But none of the food was ready yet.

6. **Why not?**

    A. The cook was tired.
    B. Mark got there too early.
    C. Mark wore a shirt and tie.
    D. Mark's father was sleeping.

Selection 7

Gloria had a big shopping bag in each hand. She climbed up three flights of stairs. She needed to stop before she got to the top.

7. **Why did Gloria stop?**

    A. She was hungry.
    B. She was poor.
    C. She was tired.
    D. She was very cold.

Selection 8

The big drum kept banging. And the cymbals went Crash! Crash! Crash! There were loud trumpets lifted high in the air. Out front, the batons went sailing in the air. A long line of hundreds of people filled the street. Mark loved to watch it all.

8. **Where was Mark?**

    A. at a big science museum
    B. at a new school
    C. at a picnic
    D. at a parade

Selection 9

Cleon is my best friend. He is near sighted and can't see very well. When I drove by him and waved, he didn't wave back.

9. **Why didn't Cleon wave back?**

    A. He was angry.
    B. He was tired.
    C. He couldn't see me.
    D. He was in a hurry.

Selection 10

It was dark. It was so dark Janet couldn't find her seat. She sat down. Suddenly, there was loud music. A big space ship sailed through the sky. She could see inside the ship where little robots were cleaning, cooking, and flying the ship. She wondered what would happen next.

10. **Where was Janet?**

    A. on the moon
    B. at a movie
    C. at an airport
    D. in a home for old people

In the rest of this unit,—

• You will decide WHO is talking.

• You will decide WHERE a story takes place.

For the following questions you will decide WHO is talking.

Selection 11

"I'm sorry. We don't have any milk left. I am expecting the truck very soon. If you can wait, we will have a new delivery of milk."

11. Who is talking?

    A. the person who runs a grocery store
    B. a woman who wants to buy milk
    C. the man who drives the milk truck
    D. a farmer who milks cows

Selection 12

"I've studied your X-rays very carefully. Your knee is broken. I will have to operate to fix it."

12. Who is talking?

    A. a mother
    B. a football player
    C. a teacher
    D. a doctor

Selection 13

"I think I've got everyone's order. One person wants eggs scrambled, one person wants bacon and eggs, and one person wants a cheese omelet. And you all want toast with breakfast."

13. Who is talking?

    A. a waiter
    B. an actor
    C. a lawyer
    D. the president of a bank

Selection 14

"I want the guitar louder in this part. The drums stay soft until the last part and then let go with everything. The piano stays in the background, playing simple chords."

14. Who is talking?

    A. the leader of a band

    B. a college teacher

    C. a bus driver

    D. a great athlete

Here you will decide WHERE something is happening.

Selection 15

The sun beat down on Nancy's back as she pushed the lawn mower back and forth. It was hard work and she was feeling hot and tired. But she couldn't rest yet. Her next chore was to weed the flowerbed.

15. Where is Nancy?

    A. in a plane

    B. in a garden

    C. on the beach

    D. in a parking lot

Selection 16

It was a perfect day to be out on the lake. There was enough wind to maintain a good speed, yet the waves were calm. Chuck lay on the deck, letting his hand trail in the water and wishing he never had to return to the harbor.

16. Where was Chuck?

    A. in a helicopter

    B. on a motor bike

    C. in a car

    D. on a sailboat

Selection 17

Ms. Jones had been on her feet since breakfast, and she has accomplished a great deal. The refrigerator was defrosted, the oven cleaned, and the floor washed and waxed. At last she could sit down and have a cup of coffee while she made up her mind about what to cook for dinner.

17. Where is Ms. Jones?

    A. in a supermarket
    B. in a department store
    C. in a kitchen
    D. in a laundromat

Selection 18

"How long will it take to replace the brake linings?" George asked.

"At least a week, maybe more," the mechanic replied.

"That long?" George cried. "What am I going to drive in the meantime?"

18. Where is George?

    A. in a shoe store
    B. in a furniture store
    C. in an auto repair shop
    D. in a doctor's office

Here you'll get practice in reading a letter and making inferences about it.

Selection 19

Dear Vicki,

I just heard you're in the hospital. I'll be back in the city next week. First thing I'll do is visit you.

Forget about fixing up the car. It's too smashed up to ever run well again.

I hope you're well soon,

Al

19a. What probably happened?

A. Vicki got sick.

B. Vicki was in a car accident.

C. Al's car need to be fixed.

D. Vicki and Al are going to take a car trip.

19b. Al didn't visit Vicki because

A. he's away.

B. he's too busy.

C. he doesn't like Vicki much.

D. he doesn't know where she is.

Selection 20

Dear Tamara,

Why are you acting like this? In school you act like you don't see me. I say something and you ignore me. Whenever I call you at home, I can't speak to you. Your brother always says you went to the movies. I can't believe you go to a movie every day.

Tell me what's happening,

Buzz

Dear Buzz,

Last Sunday we were supposed to go to the movies. We had a 2 PM date. I got on line outside in the cold and waited for you. I waited almost an hour. Then I heard you and Lenore went skating on Sunday. If you're hurting, you'd better find someone else to talk to.

Tamara

20a. Why did Buzz write a letter to Tamara?

    A. A letter is the best way to say how he feels.

    B. Tamara won't talk to him.

    C. Tamara's brother told him to write a letter.

    D. His phone is out of order.

20b. Lenore is probably

    A. Tamara's sister.

    B. Buzz's friend.

    C. a person who teaches ice skating.

    D. Tamara's mother.

20c. What probably happened?

    A. Buzz forgot his date with Tamara and went out with Lenore.

    B. Buzz was angry with Tamara and wanted her to wait in the cold.

    C. Buzz wanted to tell Lenore how much he liked Tamara.

    D. Lenore went to the wrong movie house.

Unit 7 Higher Order Reading Competencies

MAKING JUDGEMENTS

Here are some more stories where you have to pick the right answer. Sometimes the story will ask you why something happened. Sometimes you will have to decide how the story will end.

The answer isn't written in the selection. You have to figure it out.

You will read two selections. The first one will be short. The second one will be longer. If you can work out the answer to the short selection, it will help you work out the answer to the longer selection.

Look at Example 1.

Example 1

Short Selection

Something is wrong with Dad. He eats only pasta and soft food. He can't bite down hard.

1a. What is probably wrong?

A. He has a bad cold.

B. His teeth are hurting him.

C. He needs more exercise.

D. His back hurts him all the time.

Long Selection

My brother Bob has been having a lot of trouble. He bikes to school but he doesn't hear the cars when they honk at him. Last Wednesday he didn't hear an ambulance's siren until the last minute. And he plays the TV so loud that everyone else in the house shouts at him. Even our neighbor, Ms. Marles, complains about the sound from the TV.

1b. What's wrong with Bob?

    A. He doesn't get along with Ms. Marles.
    B. He doesn't know how to ride a bike.
    C. He is angry at the car drivers.
    D. He is having trouble hearing.

Example 1 gave you 2 selections. One selection was short, and the other selection was longer. But they were similar. They could both be figured out in the same way.

- In example 1, you figured out that Dad's teeth were bad.

- In example 2, you figured out that Bob couldn't hear well.

You had to make similar inferences in both the short selection and the long selection.

DRAWING CONCLUSIONS

Try Example 2.

Read the short selection and the long selection.

Select the best answer after each selection. Remember, the answer in the

short selection will help you answer the long selection.

You are asked to draw the best conclusion. That means you must figure out what is most likely to be true.

When you are done, your teacher will go over your answers.

Example 2

Short Selection

Joan lives in a very hot country. It is hot all year long.

2a. What conclusion can you make?

A. Joan is very sick.

B. Joan doesn't see very much snow.

C. Joan eats a lot of fish.

D. Joan has many friends.

 Your Teacher Will Discuss Your Answer

Long Selection

Amib lives in a very hot, dry country. High mountains surround his country. The mountains block off the clouds that carry rain. Sometimes it rains no more than a few days in the whole year. There are no rivers or big lakes in Amib's country.

2b. What conclusion can you make?

A. There are lots of tall trees, flowers, and grass in Amib's country.

B. Water in Amib's country is very valuable and never wasted.

C. Amib's favorite sport is ice-skating.

D. Many beautiful birds and fish live in Amib's country.

 Your Teacher Will Discuss Your Answer

Now you will complete the next 6 pairs of selections.

One selection will be short and one selection will be long.

The short selection will help you do the long selection.

When you've completed all six pairs of selections, your class will discuss your answers.

Selection Pair 1

Short Selection

I bought new shoes. I wore them to school. My heels turned red, and I got blisters on my toes.

1a. What probably happened?

A. Everyone in school wore sneakers.
B. The shoes were the wrong color.
C. The shoes were too tight.
D. The teachers didn't like the shoes.

Long Selection

Rhonda loves to ice skate. She knows how to go backwards and jump in the air. She just bought new figure skates. They are white with black trim and match Rhonda's ice-skating outfit. But when she put them on, they didn't feel right. Rhonda thought she would get used to them. So she continued to skate. But it wasn't much fun. After a short while, her toes hurt too much. She stopped skating and took off the skates.

1b. Rhonda's skates were probably

A. the wrong color.
B. too small.
C. too expensive.
D. too nice to use.

Selection Pair 2

Short Selection

Sherkima is the fastest runner in school. She is also a member of the math team. And she sings in the school choir.

2a. Sherkima

    A. is good at many things.

    B. lives several miles from school.

    C. doesn't have many friends.

    D. got a D in Social Studies.

Long Selection

Zack just came to America from Russia. He never even saw a baseball game until last year. But now he's on the school team. He plays first base well and he's the best hitter in the school. He's also on the football team. He's a great linebacker and he can also carry the ball.

In Russia, he played soccer and volleyball a lot. He doesn't really work harder than the other people on the team, but he never misses practice. His English is also getting better.

2b. You can conclude that Zack is

    A. very shy.

    B. good at math.

    C. lazy.

    D. a fine athlete.

Selection Pair 3

Short Selection

Aunt Mary likes watching TV. And she likes to bike. But she won't play cards and she hates checkers and chess.

3a. You can conclude that Aunt Mary

    A. is getting old.

    B. doesn't like games.

    C. eats too much.

    D. sees at least five movies a week.

Long Selection

Gabe loves to go hiking. Most summers, he spends time camping out at the lake. He likes the fresh air and cooking over an open fire. He likes to dive into the lake, even if the water is ice cold. In the winter, he spends time skiing and ice skating.

Gabe hates rainy days when he has to find something to do in the house. He doesn't care for using a computer and won't watch anything on TV. He doesn't even like to watch people ski or watch the ice skating championships. He'd rather look out of his window and wait for the rain to stop.

3b. What can you decide about Gabe?

    A. Gabe doesn't like to ski.

    B. Gabe likes computer games.

    C. Gabe likes to be outside.

    D. Gabe is lazy.

Selection Pair 4

Short Selection

Spot looked around. He sniffed the air. Nothing seemed familiar. He couldn't find his house. Where was his master?

4a. Spot was probably

A. lost.

B. sick.

C. happy.

D. hungry.

Long Selection

Marianna Houston would bike to the park to play with her friends every day she could. One day, she met some new friends. They asked her to go to a park in another part of town. Marianna wasn't sure if she should travel that far, but she went anyway. The kids rode their bikes a long way. Marianna had never seen this part of town before. They played a long game of softball.

Marianna was very tired when she started home. All the others were way ahead of her. Marianna lost sight of them. She looked around. The names of the streets were not familiar. She couldn't remember whether she should turn right or left. Everything looked very different.

4b. Marianna probably

A. enjoyed basketball more than softball.

B. didn't like her new friends.

C. didn't know her way home.

D. was the best softball player of all.

Selection Pair 5

Short Selection

Arthur's head felt very warm. His body ached. He could hardly get out of bed. He stood up but he felt so dizzy, he went back to bed. He slept all day.

5a. Arthur was probably

    A. lazy.

    B. excited.

    C. a child.

    D. sick.

Long Selection

All through the trip, the ocean was very rough. Big waves would pick up the ship and drop it back down. Every time the ship went up and down, Dorothy felt very strange. Her stomach felt like it kept going up and down. She had trouble eating anything. She wasn't the only one. No one on board wanted to eat very much.

Most people just stayed in their cabins and tried not to move too much. Even the captain said the big waves were bothering him. It was the worst trip anyone had ever taken. The waves were as big as houses.

5b. Why did Dorothy feel strange?

    A. She was seasick.

    B. The food was bad.

    C. She was worried about the Captain.

    D. She didn't stay in her cabin.

Selection Pair 6

Short Selection

The car stalled. It was the third time today. Smoke was coming out of the hood. The engine was making funny noises. Jimmy tried to start it again. It didn't move.

6a. What should you conclude?

A. Jimmy will never buy another car.

B. Something was wrong with the car.

C. The car was brand new.

D. This was the first car Jimmy ever owned.

Long Selection

Everyone was excited about the opening of the class play. The actors and prop people were ready. And the snow machine operator was getting ready, too. The class had a big new machine that made real snow. Just when the music came up, the snow machine would be turned on and snow would start to fall. It was going to be the best scene in the play.

But that's not what happened. The music started. Everybody looked up to see the snow. But there was nothing. Mr. Thomas was shouting at the man who ran the snow machine. That man was moving the handle up and down as hard as he could. He was sweating, but nothing happened. Then they brought down the curtain.

6b. What was the problem?

A. The actors didn't know their lines.

B. The operator was ill with a bad cold.

C. The play wasn't very good.

D. The snow machine didn't work.

You have completed a lot of inference questions. Now you will do two more pairs.

This time the long selection will be very long. The selections may include pictures or a title.

This will help you decide on your answers.

Remember, the short selection will help you do the longer selection.

Selection Pair 7

Short Selection

The school was completely full last year. There was barely enough room for everyone. Three hundred new students entered this year. The principal is very worried.

7a. Why is the principal worried?

A. The teachers are moving away.
B. Many of the school's windows are broken.
C. The rooms are too quiet.
D. The classrooms will be too crowded.

Long Selection

We Need Help

The New Hope Hospital was built in 1992. It was three blocks from the older hospital. New Hope was in a fine building. It could handle up to 500 patients. It had 300 patients the first year. There was plenty of room for everyone.

However, when the older hospital closed in 1994, all their patients were sent to New Hope. New Hope was very crowded that year. It took 250 new patients from the older hospital.

The situation grew worse. More and more people moved to that part of the city. New Hope Hospital grew even more crowded. There was no other hospital to care for all the people who lived in the area.

In 1996, a big new apartment house was built near the hospital. Many more people needed the hospital's help. Finally, the doctors and nurses wrote to the mayor. They said they couldn't do their jobs anymore.

7b. Why couldn't the doctors and nurses do their jobs?

A. The fire was too dangerous.

B. The food was badly cooked.

C. There were too many children playing in the halls.

D. The hospital was too crowded to help everyone.

Selection Pair 8

Short Selection

Sal has been lifting weights for 5 weeks. At first he didn't see any changes. But this week, he lifted some very heavy weights. His shirt is feeling a little tight. He even looks different.

8a. What is happening to Sal?

A. He hurt himself lifting weights.
B. He is hanging out with other weight lifters.
C. He is getting stronger muscles.
D. He is making a lot of money.

Long Selection

Something is Missing

Gloria Ruiz has always been a great tennis player. She won the State Championship nine times between 1975 and 1995. But in 1997 she didn't even finish in the top ten. She says she understands more about tennis now than she ever did before. But she doesn't win matches with her old skills.

Gloria says that her tennis racket used to feel light and ready to crush the ball. Now it feels heavy. Even her legs get tired sometimes. They never did before.

Gloria works out regularly. She exercises as much as she did in her great championship years. She still runs 5 days a week, but she runs the mile about 14 seconds slower than she did 5 years ago.

"I eat carefully. I get a lot of sleep, but I don't have my old zip," says Gloria.

She doesn't play in many tournaments anymore. She only plays about half as often as she used to. Her mind is as tough as ever; she still plays hard to win but her body isn't as capable as it once was.

8b. Why doesn't Gloria play tennis as well as she used to?

    A. She is spending too much time sleeping.
    B. She doesn't care as much.
    C. She is getting older.
    D. Her tennis racket is too heavy.

Part IV
Practice Tests

• •

You have learned many ways to improve how you read. Now you will have a chance to practice reading some longer stories. These stories are like the stories on reading tests. We hope you like reading them.

Unit 8 Practice Tests with Answer Feedback

Narrative Test 1

The Boy Next Door

Section 1

Did you ever think that there could be life on other planets? Steve never thought about it until a boy named Conrad came to live next door.

From the time Conrad and his family moved in, Steve noticed some strange things about them. Their house was full of things that Steve had never seen before. When Steve asked Conrad about them, Conrad said, "My dad likes to invent things. That's why we have so many new things."

Soon after that, Steve said to his dad, "Conrad is the smartest boy I've ever met. He seems to know things that are going to happen before they happen."

"You're imagining things," said Dad.

NOTICE: Photocopying any part of this book is forbidden by law.

95

Section 2

One week Conrad and Steve went for a hike in the hills outside the city. The hills there were quite high, and the trail was hard to climb. Some parts of it were very rocky and steep. When they stopped to rest, Conrad showed Steve something that looked like a camera.

"What does it do?" asked Steve.

"It takes X-ray pictures," said Conrad. "It's very handy when you want to look inside things like rocks and trees."

Section 3

Steve wanted to take a look, but they had to be on their way. With Conrad leading the way, the boys started to climb the steepest place.

Conrad yelled down to Steve, "Be careful! There are lots of loose rocks, and it's easy to slip."

But it was too late! Suddenly Steve felt the rocks slide under his feet. He tried to stop himself from falling, but he could not. With a crash, he tumbled down the slope. Rocks rolled under him. He landed in a bush with a thud. He tried to get up, but he could not move because of a sharp pain in his left leg.

Conrad raced down the rocky slope to help Steve. "Are you all right?" he asked.

"My leg is killing me," said Steve. "I think it's broken."

Section 4

"Stay where you are and don't move," said Conrad.

He took out his X-ray camera and used it to look at Steve's leg.

"It's broken all right," said Conrad. "But it's not too bad. I have just the thing to fix you up." He took a can of spray from his knapsack.

"This chemical can mend broken bones," said Conrad. He pressed the button and sprayed Steve's leg. In a flash, Steve felt the pain go away. He was amazed. He carefully got up and stepped on his leg. It did not hurt at all.

Section 5

"That chemical is too good to be true," said Steve. "A leg can't mend in a few seconds."

"It's something my dad invented," said Conrad. "But no one is supposed to know about it yet."

Steve thought that what Conrad said was strange. He could not see why such a good chemical should be a secret. Suddenly Steve started to put all the clues together.

He said to Conrad, "You can't fool me. No one on our planet can fix a broken leg with a chemical spray. No one can see inside things with an X-ray camera. I've thought about everything that has happened since you first arrived. And I've decided that you must be from another planet."

Section 6

Conrad smiled. He said, "You're smarter than I thought. I'm not supposed to tell anyone where we come from. But I know I can trust you, so I'll tell you. We come from another planet in the Milky Way. Your planet is thousands of years behind ours. We're here to study the history of this planet. We will stay for a few months more and then go back to our real home."

Steve was amazed to find this out. Then he asked, "Why haven't you told everyone about the chemical that mends bones and about the X-ray camera?"

"We can't let anyone know who we are," said Conrad. "If we do, we might be in danger. I hope you'll help us out by keeping silent."

Steve promised that he would never say a word about Conrad.

Section 7

Three months later, Conrad's family left for their own planet.

One evening soon after, Steve and his dad were sitting at home. Steve's dad said to him, "You know, there was something odd about that family next door. I never saw Conrad's dad mowing the lawn. Yet the grass was always cut short."

"You're imagining things, Dad," said Steve with a smile.

The Boy Next Door

1. **Look at the picture and the title. You can guess that the story is about**

   A. a boy with many pets.
   B. a boy with strange gadgets.
   C. a boy who wears funny clothes.
   D. a boy who loves baseball.

2. **Steve tumbled down the slope. Rocks rolled under him. He landed in a bush with a thud. He tried to get up, but he could not move because of a sharp pain in his left leg.**
   What had happened?

   A. Steve had fun sliding down the hill.
   B. Steve broke his leg.
   C. Steve was pushed by Conrad.
   D. Steve played a joke on Conrad.

3. **How did Conrad know that Steve's leg was broken?**

   A Conrad was a doctor.
   B. Steve was in pain.
   C. Conrad used his x-ray camera to look inside the leg.
   D. Conrad could tell by the way Steve had landed in the bush.

4. **Where did Conrad say that he got the chemical for mending bones?**

   A. He said it came from his home planet.
   B. He got it from his doctor.
   C. He bought it in a store.
   D. He said his father had invented it.

5. **In Section 5, Steve tells Conrad how he guessed that Conrad was from another planet. What clues did Steve use to figure this out?**

   A. Conrad looked very strange.
   B. Conrad's father was an inventor.
   C. The grass at Conrad's house never needed mowing.
   D. Conrad had an x-ray camera and a chemical for mending broken bones.

6. **Why were Conrad and his father visiting the Earth?**

   A. They were here to study the history of the Earth.
   B. They wanted to destroy the Earth.
   C. They wanted to rule the Earth.
   D. They wanted to give us their inventions.

7. **At the end of the story, what does Steve's dad notice about Conrad's dad?**

   A. Conrad's dad is an inventor.
   B. Conrad's dad is never at home.
   C. Conrad's dad never speaks to the neighbors.
   D. Conrad's dad never mowed the grass, but it stayed short.

8. **Why does Steve tell his dad that he is imagining things at the end of the story?**

   A. He does not want his father to know the truth.
   B. He believes his father is just imagining things.
   C. He is going to tell his father that Conrad's family is from another planet.
   D. Conrad's father really did mow the grass.

9. **Why did Conrad tell Steve that he and his family were from another planet?**

    A. Steve forced him to tell.
    B. He felt he could trust Steve.
    C. Conrad lied to scare Steve.
    D. Conrad made up the whole story as a joke.

10. **What was Conrad like?**

    A. He looked like a person from another planet.
    B. He was not friendly to Steve.
    C. He did not want to help Steve when he was hurt.
    D. He looked and acted like an ordinary boy.

11. **Why does Steve smile at the end of the story?**

    A. He knows that Conrad cut the grass.
    B. His father knows the family next door is from another planet.
    C. His father knows that Conrad has an x-ray machine.
    D. He says the same thing to his father that his father had said to him.

12. **Look at Section 1. What did Steve find strange about Conrad's house?**

    A. It had strange furniture.
    B. It looked different than the other houses.
    C. It had inventions inside that Steve had never seen before.
    D. The family ate strange food.

13. **How did Steve break his leg?**

    A. He was skiing.
    B. Conrad pushed him.
    C. He fell down a rocky slope.
    D. He played with Conrad's x-ray machine.

Answer Feedback

In this section you will see if you answered the questions correctly. Your teacher may want to discuss your answers and those of the other students in your class.

One good strategy is to **PROVE YOUR ANSWER.** You find the part of the selection you used to answer a question. Sometimes you will find the words you needed right there on the page. Other times, the answer is found in two or more sentences. You need to **SEARCH** and **THINK** in several places.

Sometimes your answer comes from thinking about and summing up what the author said. This is the best way to answer questions about theme and main idea.

Other times you must use your **OWN EXPERIENCE.** For example, some questions ask you to use a vocabulary word in a new sentence. You must use your own experience to decide which answer makes most sense.

1. **The correct choice is B.** You can see that the boy in the picture is carrying a strange gadget or machine. None of the other choices are related to the picture.

2. **The correct choice is B.** The sharp pain comes from a broken leg. The selection says he fell down the slope and injured his leg.

3. This is another question that you can answer right from the story. In the second paragraph of Section 4, Conrad takes out his x-ray camera to see inside Steve's leg. He sees the broken bone *inside* Steve's leg. Choice D could not be right. **Choice C is the right one.**

4. The answer is in Section 5. Conrad claims his father invented the spray, so you know **Choice D is correct.** Conrad does **not** tell Steve that he got the spray from his home planet at this point in the story. That happens later on. So Choice A is wrong.

5. This is another question where you must look at the right part of the story. The question tells you to look at Section 5 to see what Steve thinks of Conrad at this time. He doesn't think Conrad looks strange. He doesn't yet know about the grass at Conrad's house. So Choices A and C are wrong. **Choice D** repeats the clues Conrad used to solve the mystery.

6. You must decide why Conrad and his family are visiting the Earth. Choices B and C are never mentioned in the story. Choice D is wrong because they are keeping their inventions secret. **Choice A is right.**

7. This question also tells you where to look for the answer. Choice A is something Steve's dad may know. But Choice D is the one mentioned in the last part of the story, Section 7. Choices B and C are never mentioned in the story. **Choice D is the answer.**

8. This question asks you to draw a conclusion. But, in this case, you have plenty of information. You must **SEARCH** for this information and **THINK** about it to come up with an answer. Conrad told Steve not to tell anyone that his family is from another planet. Steve promised to keep it a secret. So you can conclude that Steve wants his father to think he is just imagining things. **Choice A is the right one.**

9. This is another character question. You are asked why a character did something. You know from the story that Conrad was trying to hide the fact that he and his family were from another planet. So why does he tell Steve the truth? You know from your reading that the boys were good friends. And you know from your own experience that good friends trust each other. So **Choice B makes the most sense.** You can also answer this question by crossing out choices you know are wrong. Conrad was not lying or joking. So Choices C and D are wrong. Steve *guessed* the truth, but he never forced Conrad to tell him. So Choice B is wrong, too. Only **Choice B makes sense.**

10. You can also cross out choices to answer this question. You know from the story that Conrad was friendly. He also helped Steve when he was hurt. So Choices B and C are wrong. The story does **not** say that Conrad looked like a person from another planet. Your sense tells you that Conrad must have looked like everyone else, or he would have been found out. So **Choice D is the right one.**

11. This is another question that to answer you must **SEARCH** through the selection and **THINK**. If you look back to Section 1, you can find the same words that Steve is now saying. Steve's father told him at the beginning of the story that he was imagining things, too. So **Choice D is the right one.**

12. The answer to this question is right there in Section 1. The second paragraph tells you that Steve notices something strange in Conrad's house. The house is full of inventions that Steve has never seen anywhere else. **Choice C is correct.**

13. What **caused** Steve to break his leg? The answer is right there in Section 3. In the third paragraph, you read that Steve slipped on rocks while climbing a rocky slope. **The right answer is C.**

Informational Test 1

Animals in Motion

Section 1

The Fastest Animals

Which animal is the fastest? On land, it's the cheetah. The cheetah is a large, slim cat with yellow fur and black spots. Cheetahs hunt antelopes. Antelopes can run about 50 miles an hour. The cheetah is the only animal that can run faster than that.

A hungry cheetah will carefully study an antelope herd. If the cheetah sees an antelope that looks sick or weak, it races toward it. But often the cheetah doesn't catch the antelope right away. And it can't keep up its top speed for very long. The cheetah slows down to about 40 miles an hour after a minute or so. A healthy antelope can get away.

Section 2

Some sea animals can also move quickly, though not as quickly as a cheetah! Whales and dolphins swim through the ocean at up to 25 miles an hour. A tuna, one of the fastest fish, can swim at 43 miles an hour.

Insects can be surprisingly fast, too. Monarch butterflies can fly at more than 20 miles an hour! That's very fast for such a tiny creature. These butterflies move almost as fast as an elephant can run.

But the fastest of all animals are birds. And the fastest bird is the falcon. It's a kind of hawk that can fly at 180 miles an hour. It swoops down quickly to kill small birds and mice.

Section 3

Speedsters in the Air

Why do birds move faster than other animals? One reason is their shape. Birds are *streamlined*. This means that their bodies are shaped so that air flows past them smoothly. They just slip through the air. That helps them fly swiftly. In addition, when birds fly, they usually tuck their legs and feet close to their bodies. This also adds to the streamlined effect.

Finally, birds don't weigh much. Their feathers and bones are hollow. And they are very strong for their size.

Of course, not all birds use their wings for high-speed performance. The tiny hummingbird has special wings. It is able to fly forward, backward, or up and down. It can even *hover* in the air without going anywhere like a helicopter.

Section 4

How Some Animals Move on Land

Animals have many ways of moving on land. The fastest animals have legs that are very long compared to the size of their bodies. Animals with extra-long legs include horses, ostriches, zebras, and greyhounds—and of course, cheetahs and antelopes.

On the other hand, salamanders have long bodies with very small, short legs. They have to wiggle their bodies to help move these tiny legs along the ground. They can't move fast at all.

Section 5

Animals use their legs to move in more ways than just running. Frogs cannot stand up or walk, but they can use their strong back legs to move in long leaps. Some frogs can easily jump five feet at a time.

The champion jumper is the red kangaroo. It can cover 30 feet in one hop. Its powerful legs act like springs. They bounce the animal up and forward.

Section 6

Strange Feet

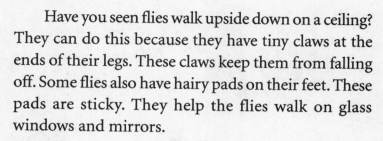

Have you seen flies walk upside down on a ceiling? They can do this because they have tiny claws at the ends of their legs. These claws keep them from falling off. Some flies also have hairy pads on their feet. These pads are sticky. They help the flies walk on glass windows and mirrors.

Snails also have "sticky feet." A snail has a single flat foot that puts out sticky fluid. The snail glides along on its own sticky trail.

Some sea creatures have strange feet also. Starfish and sea urchins have tube feet with a *suction cup* at the end of each tube. These animals use the cups to hold on to things. Then they push or pull their bodies along.

Section 7

Tails, Flippers, Fins, and Squirts

Have you ever tried to walk in water up to your chin? If so, you know it's hard. Only streamlined animals can move quickly through water.

Whales move through the water by moving their tails up and down. So do dolphins and porpoises. They use their front flippers to keep their balance and to turn. Most fish, however, swim by moving their tails from side to side, not up and down. They use their front fins for balance just the way dolphins use their flippers.

Section 8

The octopus has a special way of swimming. Its body is like a soft bag. It usually swims slowly by taking water into its body and then squirting it out again. The squirt goes one way, and the octopus goes the other. When it is frightened, the octopus pushes water out of its body very hard. That makes it shoot backward very quickly.

Whether they fly, walk, hop, jump, wiggle, or slide, animals move every day of their lives. They move to find food, to run from their enemies, and sometimes, just for the fun of it.

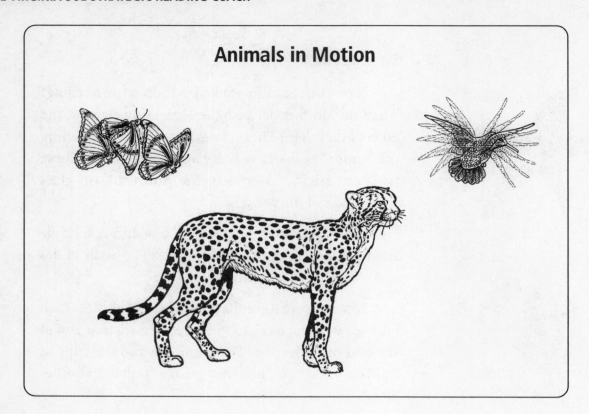

Animals in Motion

1. **Look at the picture and the title. You can guess that the story is about**

   A. different animals and how they move.
   B. what animals like to eat.
   C. how animals escape from their enemies.
   D. which animals make good pets.

2. **Birds weigh very little.**
   They have hollow bones.
   Their bodies are shaped so air goes past them swiftly.
   They are very strong.

   These facts help us understand why

   A. birds are so pretty.
   B. people like birds.
   C. birds can swim.
   D. birds can fly quickly.

3. **Suppose the cheetah and the antelope had a race. The race was for just half of a city block. Who would win the race?**

   A. The cheetah would win.
   B. The antelope would win.
   C. It would be a tie.
   D. Neither could run that far.

4. **A cheetah runs for 5 minutes. When does it run the fastest?**

   A. during the first minute
   B. after about 2 minutes
   C. after 4 minutes
   D. at the end of the 5 minutes

5. **Under which heading do you find information about the sticky feet of flies?**

   A. How Some Animals Move
   B. Strange Feet
   C. Wings Increase Speed
   D. Tails, Flippers, and Fins

6. **Look back at the heading "How Some Animals Move on Land." What is the main idea of the two paragraphs in Section 5 that tell about frogs and kangaroos?**

   A. The fastest animals have long legs.
   B. Frogs can not stand on their legs.
   C. Animals with legs have many ways of moving.
   D. A kangaroo moves by hopping.

7. **Which of these creatures use sticky matter to help them "walk" in different places?**

   A. bats and birds
   B. salamanders
   C. starfish and sea urchins
   D. flies and snails

8. In Section 3, you learn that birds are *streamlined*. What does this mean?

    A. They do not have wings.
    B. Their bodies have a shape that helps them fly faster.
    C. They use their legs when they fly.
    D. They weigh very little.

9. You also learned that a humming bird can *hover* in the air like a helicopter. Which is an example of *hovering* in the air?

    A. staying in one spot
    B. flying forward
    C. flying backward
    D. flying up and down

10. What do animals in the water mainly use their tails for?

    A. to keep their balance
    B. to shoot backward
    C. to move forward through the water
    D. to turn in another direction

11. What is the central purpose of this selection?

    A. to tell about interesting animals
    B. to show how an antelope can escape from a cheetah
    C. to tell about how animals move in different ways
    D. to tell how birds fly

12. How does an octopus move through water?

    A. It uses its fins and tail.
    B. It fills its body with water and shoots it out.
    C. It swims by moving its long arms.
    D. It uses its tail only.

13. **Which group of animals is the fastest?**

   A. birds
   B. insects
   C. animals with long legs
   D. fish

14. **You read that starfish have tube feet with a *suction cup* on the end. How does a *suction cup* work?**

   A. The suction cup pulls food in.
   B. The suction cup pushes things out of the way.
   C. The suction cup grips onto things.
   D. The suction cup pulls water inside the animal's body.

15. **Which animal can move the fastest?**

   A. the cheetah
   B. the whale
   C. the tuna
   D. the falcon

16. **It is hard for a cheetah to catch a healthy antelope because**

   A. after running for a while, the cheetah has to slow down.
   B. antelopes run much faster than cheetahs.
   C. the cheetah is not as strong as the antelope.
   D. the cheetah is often lazy.

Answer Feedback

In this section you will learn the correct answers to the questions about how animals move. You will have a chance to discuss your answers with your teacher. You may also compare your answers with those of the other students in your class.

1. **The correct answer is A.** The pictures show different animals and how they move. None of the other choices are related to the picture. The title is: "Animals in Motion," which means "animals moving."

2. **The correct answer is D.** Each of these facts tells why birds can fly quickly. The facts do not fit any of the other answers.

3. This question gives you a problem to solve. You have to use what you know from the article to solve the problem. You read in Section 1 that a cheetah can run faster than an antelope, but can only run for a short time. When it first races after an antelope, it has a good chance of catching it. A half of a city block is not a long distance, and would be a very short race. Even though the antelope is fast, the cheetah could beat it in a short run. So **Choice A is right.**

4. You will use the same information from Section 1 to answer this question. You read that the cheetah can run very fast at first. Later, after the first minute, it slows down. This means that it is fastest in the first minute. So **Choice A is the only answer.**

5. This question asks you to find certain information. Then you have to find the heading that information is under. One clue is the word **feet** in the question. Information about the sticky feet of flies is under **Choice B—"Strange Feet."**

6. Choice A is not in Section 5. Choices B and D give details but not the main idea. The main idea is: Animals use their legs to move in different ways. **This matches Choice C.**

7. The answer is in Section 6. Flies and snails are the creatures with sticky feet. **Choice D is correct.**

8. The answer is right there in Section 3. You read that birds' bodies are shaped so that air flows past them quickly. **This means the same as Choice B:** Their bodies have a shape that helps them fly. Choices C and D are true of birds. But they do not fit the meaning of *streamlined*.

9. This is another vocabulary question. It gives you an example of the meaning of the word from the selection. Then it asks you to find another example in the choices. You can check back to the sentence in Section 3 that describes *hovering*. So you can tell that **Choice A is the right one.**

10. To answer the question, you must **SEARCH** and **THINK.** In Section 7, you read that whales, porpoises, and dolphins move through the water by pushing their tails up and down. You also read that fish swim by pushing their tails from side to side. Both of these are examples of animals using their tails to **push** themselves forward through the water. So **Choice C is the best.** Choices A, B, and D tell about other movements animals make in water using other parts of their bodies.

11. This question asks you about the central purpose of the selection. **Choice C summarizes what the selection is about:** the different ways animals move.

12. The answer to this question is right there in Section 8. **The correct choice is B.**

13. This question asks about information you read in the beginning of the selection. **Choice A is right.**

14. This is another vocabulary question. You can locate the vocabulary phrase *suction cup* in dark letters in Section 6. From the information in Section 6, you can see that *suction cups* hold onto things. They help the animal pull its body along. **Choice C says the same thing.**

15. This answer is right in the selection. You read about many fast-moving animals. But only one is called the fastest. Section 2 tells you that birds are the fastest animals and the fastest bird is the falcon, **Choice D.** This question can trip up a student who is not careful to **READ ALL THE ANSWER CHOICES.** You read that cheetahs are very fast animals. But you must read all the choices to find the fastest of all—the falcon.

16. This answer is also right in the selection. In Section 1, you read that the cheetah loses speed after running for a while. This means that it slows down. So **Choice A is correct.**

Unit 9 Practice Tests 2

Narrative Test 2

The Emperor's Nightingale

Section 1

The emperor of China lived in the finest palace in the world. His garden was huge. At the end of the garden were some cool green woods.

A nightingale lived in the middle of these woods. When the bird sang, all who heard it stopped to listen and *marvel* at its song. There was nothing finer in all of China than the song of this nightingale.

Travelers came to China from all over the world. They admired the emperor's palace and his garden. But most of all, they admired the nightingale's song. People wrote books about their travels to China. And they all said that the nightingale was the most wonderful thing in all of China.

Section 2

One afternoon the emperor was reading one of these books. It was the first time he had heard about the nightingale. "How can it be that the nightingale lives in my garden and I have never heard it sing?" the emperor shouted to the chief of his guards. "Bring this nightingale to me now!"

"But, Your Majesty," said the chief of the guards, "I don't know where it is."

"I insist upon hearing the nightingale sing tonight!" shouted the emperor. "So find it. If you do not, I will have your head!"

Section 3

The chief of the guards wanted to keep his head. So he ran off in search of someone who had heard the nightingale. At last, he found a kitchen maid who knew where the nightingale lived. Then he and the kitchen maid set off to find the bird.

After a while, the chief of the guards and the kitchen maid came to the tree where the nightingale lived. And the bird began to sing.

"Oh! What a sound!" they sighed.

The chief of the guards picked up the nightingale and took it to the emperor's palace.

When the emperor heard the nightingale sing, he wept with joy. "I have never heard anything like it!" he said. "I'm going to keep this bird with me forever."

Section 4

From that day on, the nightingale lived in a golden cage at the emperor's palace. The bird was free to go out of the cage for a walk three times a day. But when it did, it was followed by ten guards. Each guard held on to a ribbon that was tied to the bird's leg. The nightingale was very unhappy because it could not fly.

Then one day a package arrived from the emperor of Japan. Inside the package was a wonderful toy nightingale. It was made out of silver and gold and pearls and rubies. After it was wound up, the toy bird sang a song just like the one the real bird sang.

The emperor was pleased with his gift. He knew the real nightingale wanted to go back to its home. So he freed it, and it flew back to its tree in the woods.

Section 5

A year passed. The emperor liked the toy nightingale very much. The toy bird was pretty to look at. And it could sing the same song over and over without getting tired. But one evening the toy bird broke down.

The emperor sent for a toy maker who fixed the toy as well as he could. But he told the emperor the sad news. "The bird is so worn out," he said, "that it can only sing one day a year."

Section 6

Five years passed, and the emperor became ill. The royal doctors did everything in their power to cure him.

But the emperor got worse and worse. At last, the doctors thought that the time had come for him to die.

The emperor, too, thought he was going to die. He asked everyone to leave his room. Then he lay on his bed and looked at the toy nightingale sitting beside him.

"Sing for me one last time," he said in a faint voice.

But the toy bird could not sing. No one was there to wind it. The emperor was too weak to wind it himself. So he just lay back on his pillow.

Section 7

Suddenly a song floated in from a tree outside the emperors window. It was the real nightingale! The nightingale had heard the emperor was ill. So it came to sing to the emperor. The song it sang was so wonderful that the emperor began to feel better. "I will keep you here with me always," he said to the nightingale.

When the nightingale heard this, it grew very unhappy. It wanted to be free. But the emperor cried as loudly as he could, "No! Don't go! Stay for a while. Your singing is bringing back my strength. I will let you be free to live in the woods. Just come back now and then and sing to me."

Section 8

The nightingale stayed and sang until the emperor was strong again.

The next day the chief of the emperor's guards came to the emperor's room dressed in black. He thought the emperor had died in the night. But he found him standing by his window. The emperor had a smile on his face, and he was looking out at the woods far away.

The Emperor's Nightingale

1. **Look at the picture and the title. You would guess this story is about**

    A. the children of a rich emperor.
    B. an emperor who wrote many poems.
    C. a real bird and a toy bird that sang for an emperor.
    D. a story about a zoo that had birds and animals.

2. **In Section 7, the real nightingale came back to sing for the emperor. Why did he do this?**

    A. He heard that the emperor was sick.
    B. He wanted to show that he was better than a toy.
    C. He liked to show off his voice.
    D. He wanted to move back to the palace.

3. **What was special about the real nightingale?**

    A. It was covered with jewels.
    B. It came from China.
    C. It never wore out.
    D. It sang beautifully.

4. **How did the emperor find out about the real nightingale?**

   A. He saw it in the woods.
   B. He read about it in a book.
   C. The kitchen maid told him about it.
   D. The chief of his guards told him about it.

5. **Why was the real nightingale unhappy living in the palace?**

   A. He wanted to be free to fly.
   B. He did not like singing.
   C. The emperor was not kind to him.
   D. He did not like the emperor.

6. **Why did the emperor keep the toy nightingale instead of the real one?**

   A. It was a gift from a king.
   B. It knew many more songs than the real nightingale.
   C. He liked to wind it up.
   D. It could sing all day long, and did not need to be free.

7. **You read in Section 4 that the emperor got a toy nightingale. Then he let the real nightingale go back to the forest. How did the bird feel about that?**

   A. sad because the emperor did not want him
   B. sad to leave the beautiful palace
   C. glad to be free and to go home
   D. jealous of the toy nightingale

8. **Why did the toy bird NOT sing for the sick emperor?**

   A. It was completely broken.
   B. It did not want to sing.
   C. It had forgotten how to sing.
   D. The emperor was too weak to wind up the toy.

9. **The kitchen maid**

    A. cooked meals for the nightingale.
    B. knew how to cure the emperor.
    C. never went into the emperor's garden.
    D. knew where the nightingale lived.

10. **In Section 7, why does the real nightingale become unhappy?**

    A. because he knows the emperor will die
    B. because the emperor wants to keep him in the palace again
    C. because he is sad that the toy nightingale is broken
    D. because he does not know what to sing to the emperor

11. **At the end of the story, the emperor looks at the woods and smiles. What is the emperor thinking about?**

    A. how he loves the real nightingale's song
    B. how much money he owns
    C. how beautiful the toy nightingale is
    D. how much he likes his doctor

12. **What kind of story is "The Emperor's Nightingale"?**

    A. a true story
    B. a fairy tale
    C. a biography
    D. a nature story

13. **Look at the second paragraph in Section 1. Here you read that everyone who heard the real nightingale would *marvel* at its song. What does *marvel* mean?**

    A. be amazed
    B. be bored with
    C. not like
    D. sing along with

NOTICE: Photocopying any part of this book is forbidden by law.

117

Informational Test 2

Egypt Long Ago

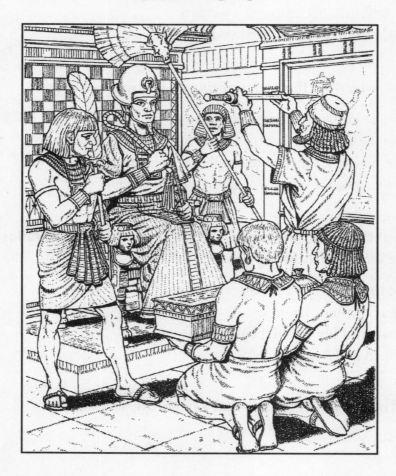

About five thousand years ago, a great civilization was born. It was in Egypt near the Nile River. The Nile is the longest river in the world. It is 4,000 miles long. It is also special for another reason. Every year, the river overflows. The rich dirt in the river is washed onto the river banks. This makes the land very good for farming.

The people of Egypt were able to grow a lot of food. They even had extra food to store away for the future. Because there was so much food, some people did not have to be farmers. Some people could spend their time making tools or weaving cloth. Some became leaders of religion or government.

The Egyptians used their extra food, tools, and cloth for trade with people of other countries. One country that Egypt traded with was Nubia. Nubia was to the south of Egypt along the Nile River, and it was very rich in gold. Egypt and Nubia both developed important civilizations.

The Pharaoh of Egypt

Egypt was ruled by kings called *pharaohs* [FAIR ohz]. Egyptians believed that their pharaoh was a god. Every morning he or she performed a special ceremony and said certain prayers. The people believed that the pharaoh's prayers kept the people safe. They also believed that the prayers of the pharaoh made the Nile overflow every year. Without the pharaoh, they thought there would not be enough food.

The first pharaoh is said to be Menes [MEE-neez]. He was the king of southern Egypt. He brought the two parts of Egypt together and made them one country. Menes ruled from his capital city of Memphis. He had complete power of life or death over everyone. He made all the laws. He owned all the land.

The pharaohs had advisors. Most of them were nobles. The nobles could be priests. They also could be royal governors, who ruled far-away parts of Egypt. All of the pharaohs were men except one. A woman named Hatshepsut (haht-SHEP-soot) ruled as pharaoh for 22 years. Women among the nobles could be priestesses and serve in the temples.

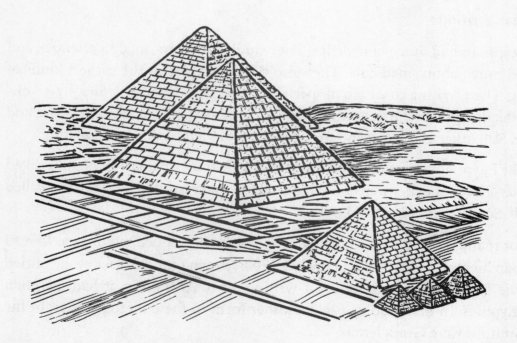

The Pyramids

Many early pharaohs were buried in tombs inside or underneath pyramids. If you travel to Egypt today, you can still see some of these pyramids standing. They are huge buildings with four sides. Each side is shaped like a triangle. It took about 20 years and much work by many thousands of people to build a pyramid.

The Egyptians believed that there was a wonderful life after death. They believed that the dead went to a land where they spent their time eating, drinking, and visiting with friends and family. The pharaoh was buried inside his or her tomb with all the things he or she needed for this wonderful life. There were clothes, food, jewelry, furniture, and games in the tomb. One tomb of a pharaoh had a complete boat in it. Nobles also had tombs filled with beautiful belongings.

Tombs were hidden inside or under the pyramids. The kings wanted to make sure that no one stole their valuable belongings. Many of these belongings were made of gold. Some had precious jewels on them. The pyramids were meant to be *monuments*. They were to remind the people of the greatness of the person buried there.

The Egyptians wanted to keep the bodies of the dead from decaying. They thought that the dead would need their bodies in the *afterlife*. They dried out the dead body. Then they bandaged it with long strips of linen. This dried body is called a *mummy*. Many mummies have been found in the pyramids of Egypt. The bodies have not completely decayed. Scientists have learned many things from studying these bodies.

Egyptian Writing

Egyptians had much knowledge. They studied the stars, made a calendar, and learned much about medicine. They also developed one of the earliest kinds of writing. Their writing consisted of special pictures called *hieroglyphics* [hy-er-oh-GLIF-ihks]. Some pictures stand for things. Others stand for ideas like love and justice. Still other pictures stand for sounds, just as letters do in our writing.

The Egyptians wrote on paper that they made from a plant. The plant is called *papyrus*. Pieces of paper were joined together to make a roll. A long roll was called a *scroll*. Scrolls were Egyptian books.

For many centuries after Egyptian civilization had ended, no one could read Egyptian hieroglyphics. Then, in the late 1700s, a man found a black stone buried near the Nile. It had three kinds of writing on it. At the top, it had Egyptian hieroglyphics. In the middle, it had another form of these hieroglyphics. In the bottom third were Greek letters.

Since some people could read Greek writing, they were able to figure out the message. Then they were about to find out what the hieroglyphics meant. They spelled out the same message that was written in Greek. By studying this stone, called the Rosetta Stone, people learned to understand many Egyptian hieroglyphics. They were able to read the writing on tombs, temples, and palaces. Most of the paper scrolls were gone. But they were still able to learn a lot about the Egyptians of old.

The great civilization of the Egyptians lasted for three thousand years. Today we are still amazed by the pyramids, temples, and works of art that the Egyptians left behind.

Egypt Long Ago

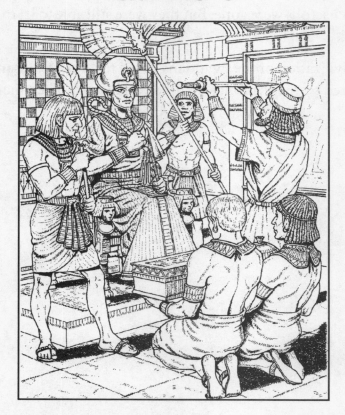

1. **Look at the picture and the title. You can guess this selection will discuss**

    A. the gold statues of Egypt.
    B. the way Egypt fought in war.
    C. the kings of Egypt and how great they were.
    D. the ways to treat sickness first discovered in Egypt.

2. **The Nile River overflows each year. It brings a lot of good soil to the farm land. This is important because**

    A. the soil was needed to make the pyramids.
    B. papyrus was made from rich soil.
    C. the Rosetta Stone came from the Nile River.
    D. Egypt was able to grow a lot of extra food.

3. **How did the Nile River make the land rich?**

   A. The water had gold in it.
   B. The Nile overflowed and made the land good for farming.
   C. The Nile River was very long.
   D. People raised crops in the water.

4. **What happened in Egypt due to the extra food they were able to grow?**

   A. Everyone had to be a farmer.
   B. Some people could do work besides farming.
   C. The people were all rich.
   D. They did not store any food away.

5. **Which of these statements did you NOT read in the selection?**

   A. The people thought the pharaoh was a god.
   B. The pharaoh said special prayers every morning.
   C. The pharaoh had complete power over everyone.
   D. The Nile did what the pharaoh told it to do.

6. **What is the most important idea in this selection?**

   A. The Egyptians buried pharaohs in pyramids.
   B. The Egyptians knew how to write.
   C. The Egyptians had an important civilization.
   D. Egypt is on the Nile River.

7. **Which of these statements is NOT true?**

   A. Menes was the first pharaoh.
   B. Religious leaders were all men.
   C. Nobles could be governors.
   D. A woman could be a pharaoh.

8. **Pyramids were used**

    A. for farms.
    B. as churches.
    C. to bury pharaohs.
    D. to train the army.

9. **How do we know that Egyptians believed people lived another life after death?**

    A. They buried their kings.
    B. Many articles in the tombs were made of gold.
    C. They filled the tombs with the person's belongings and with food.
    D. Pyramids were very large.

10. **What best describes what hieroglyphics are?**

    A. picture writing
    B. writing with our alphabet
    C. writing on clay tablets
    D. writing with chalk

11. **How did modern people learn to read hieroglyphics?**

    A. The Egyptians left a book explaining their writing.
    B. They found Egyptian paper scrolls.
    C. They learned from pictures in temples.
    D. They found a stone that helped them read the hieroglyphics.

12. **Why is the pharaoh Menes important?**

    A. He was the last pharaoh.
    B. The Egyptians thought he protected the people.
    C. He made one country out of the two parts of Egypt.
    D. Menes was a female pharaoh.

13. **Why did the Egyptians create mummies?**

    A. They wanted to show people the pharaoh's body.
    B. They wanted to protect the body from snow and ice.
    C. They wanted to save the body from wild animals.
    D. They believed people needed their bodies in the afterlife.

14. **Which of these statements is NOT a reason that Egypt traded with Nubia?**

    A. The Egyptians needed Nubian horses.
    B. Nubia had lots of gold.
    C. The Egyptians wanted goods that the Nubians made.
    D. Nubia was very close to Egypt.